W
wool

U
underwear

M
mittens

L leotards

K
knits

I
ice skates

F
fabric

E ensemble

C
costumes

D Is for Dress-Up

THE ABC'S OF WHAT WE WEAR

××× by Maria Carluccio ×××

chronicle books · san francisco

For Mom

Special thanks to Ariel, Kelly, Kayla, and Tara for all your amazingly supportive guidance.

Copyright © 2016 by Maria Carluccio.
All rights reserved. No part of this book may be reproduced in any form without written permission from the publisher.

Library of Congress Cataloging-in-Publication Data:

Carluccio, Maria, author.
D is for dress up : the ABC's of what we wear / by Maria Carluccio.
pages cm
Audience: Ages 3-5.
ISBN 978-1-4521-4025-4
1. Clothing and dress—Juvenile literature. 2. English language—Alphabet—Juvenile literature. 3. Alphabet books. I. Title.
TX340.C27 2016
391—dc23
2015017755

Manufactured in China.

Design by Tara Creehan and Kayla Ferriera.
Typeset in Filosofia.
The illustrations in this book were rendered digitally.

10 9 8 7 6 5 4 3 2 1

Chronicle Books LLC
680 Second Street
San Francisco, California 94107

Chronicle Books—we see things differently.
Become part of our community at www.chroniclekids.com.